Photograph of G. Verdi, signed and inscribed to
Gustav Schirmer, founder of the house

OTELLO

Lyric Drama in Four Acts

Music by

Giuseppe Verdi

Libretto by
ARRIGO BOITO
(Founded on Shakespeare's tragedy)

English Version by
WALTER DUCLOUX

ED. 2936

G. SCHIRMER
New York/London

Note

G. SCHIRMER, INC.

OTELLO

Giuseppe Verdi (1813-1901) had been an admirer of Shakespeare from his earliest youth. He frequently read and re-read the Bard's plays, sometimes for sheer enjoyment and more often in search of a libretto. After *Macbeth*, written when Verdi was only 34, he worked for years on a musical setting of *King Lear*, only to abandon the project after many frustrations.

Verdi had long been interested in Shakespeare's dramatization of a true incident involving one Giacomo Moro who had murdered his wife in a fit of jealousy. Mistaking his name for an indication of his race, Shakespeare had made him into *The Moor of Venice*. For many years, Verdi was even more fascinated by the figure of Iago whom he saw as "a tall, thin man with a receding forehead and narrow-set eyes, nonchalant and perfunctory in manner." At first, Iago was to be the title-hero; in addition to Verdi's interest in him, one reason was the composer's reverence for Rossini, whose *Otello* still held the stage all over Europe and was considered a masterpiece.

By the time Verdi felt himself ready for the task, the 70-year-old composer's mastery had fully matured. His still prodigious inventiveness was harnessed by the stern self-discipline of one whose artistic aims were crystal-clear. It was no longer a question of Verdi's doing justice to Shakespeare: The musician and the playwright were now dwelling on equal heights.

The man who found the formula to fuse the two into one was Arrigo Boito, brilliant poet and literary mind and a successful opera composer as well. In the course of his climb to the summit Verdi's demands on his librettists had steadily grown. He now demanded poetry intimately attuned to a new, free-flowing melodic line, punctuated by "la parola drammatica," the verbal thrust unfettered by any restrictions but the demands of the drama. In Boito, Verdi found a collaborator almost thirty years his junior but fully able to live up to his ideals.

Boito went straight to the core of Shakespeare's dramatic strength, stripping the plot of its political byplay and of a number of subsidiary characters. Aware of the powers of intensification given to music, he created opportunities for dramatic climaxes unknown to the spoken stage: Choruses, ensembles, and solo-passages underlined by orchestral commentary.

The world-premiere of *Otello* took place at La Scala in Milan on February 5, 1887. Francesco Tamagno portrayed the Moor and Victor Maurel was Iago. Worried about its stage-worthiness, Verdi had wrung a unique concession from the management: That he could withdraw the work even after the final dress-rehearsal if it did not live up to his expectations. His cautions proved unnecessary: Long before the final curtain, the audience, including many distinguished visitors from abroad, had given its verdict by tumultuous demonstrations after every act, making the first performance of *Otello* one of the greatest triumphs in Verdi's long career.

Within little more than a year, *Otello* was performed in New York by an Italian company especially assembled for that purpose. The Metropolitan presented the work for the first time in 1891, with Tamagno in the title-role. A year later, Jean de Reszké portrayed the role, soon to be followed by other distinguished artists. In 1909, *Otello* introduced to America one of the most celebrated Moors of Venice, Leo Slezak. On that occasion, the conductor was Arturo Toscanini, himself a veteran of the world-premiere in Milan, where he was a member of the cello-section of the orchestra. The list of notable interpreters of Iago includes most of the famous names from the baritone roster, including Lawrence Tibbett and Leonard Warren.

W.D.

THE STORY

ACT I. Amid thunder and lightning, the people of Cyprus anxiously observe the predicament of a storm-tossed vessel bearing their governor, Otello, on his return from a crucial battle against the Turks. The ship makes port, to the relief of everyone except Iago, an ensign in the service of Otello who had hoped for the latter's death. Tumultuously welcomed, the dark-skinned hero announces victory over the heathens. While the populace prepares for a celebration, Iago reveals his true feelings to Roderigo, a nobleman hopelessly in love with Otello's wife, Desdemona. Iago feels slighted by the fact that the young and handsome Cassio was promoted by Otello and wishes to take revenge on both of them. Roderigo is to involve Cassio in a drunken brawl, thus spoiling both Cassio's unblemished record and Otello's reunion with his wife. Iago's exuberant drinking-song soon has its desired effect on Cassio. In his cups, he is unable to take charge of his duties. Reprimanded by another officer, Montano, Cassio assaults and wounds him. Otello, called on the scene by the commotion, strips Cassio of his rank just as Desdemona joins him. Iago is to take command and restore order. Otello and Desdemona, alone at last under the star-studded sky, reminisce about the early days of their acquaintance and reaffirm their love for each other. Overcome by emotion, the Moor trembles at the thought that they are now living a moment of such sublime happiness that Destiny might never grant them another such hour. Kissing his wife three times, he leads her back into the castle as the morningstar heralds the dawn of a new day.

ACT II. Feigning concern for Cassio's plight, Iago advises him to seek Desdemona's help in order to return into the good graces of Otello. After Cassio leaves, Iago soliloquizes on his functions as a tool of the Spirit of Evil. For him, honor, friendship and love are but meaningless figments of human delusion, and death will be the end of everything. His musings are over when he notices Desdemona who is approached by Cassio. He takes his leave just as Otello enters the hall. Otello's perfunctory question about the man who just left Desdemona gives Iago the cue. He soon succeeds in arousing the Moor's suspicion. Graciously accepting the homage of the people of Cyprus, Desdemona and Emilia, her lady-in-waiting and the wife of Iago, enter the hall. Otello's suspicion is immediatey reinforced when his wife starts pleading Cassio's cause. In a fit of anger Otello rejects Desdemona's attempt to soothe his discomfort and throws her handkerchief to the ground. Iago, quick to spot possible evidence to support his web of lies, wrenches the handkerchief from Emilia's hand. After the women leave, Iago, masterfully manipulating Otello's torn mind, pretends to risk his master's wrath by offering his services in order to help confirm or allay the Moor's suspicions, using every opportunity to arouse Otello's jealousy while warning him of jealousy as a passion against which there is no cure. Otello, nearly convinced of his wife's treachery, swears to take revenge. In this oath he is joined by Iago whose own revenge against Otello is already well underway.

ACT III. Awaiting the arrival of a delegation from Venice, Iago continues to spin his intrigue. Having played the handkerchief into the hands of Cassio, he now proceeds to have Otello see it in Cassio's possession. While he goes out to fetch the unsuspecting Cassio, Otello is joined by his wife. Remaining outwardly calm, Otello soon traps Desdemona into admitting that she does not have the fateful object with her. He warns her of the terrible consequences if she should ever lose it, then orders her to bring it at once. Confused, Desdemona starts to leave, but soon she turns back to him, gently scolding him for feigning anger in order

v

to ward off her pleading for Cassio. Her naively repeated plea shatters Otello's composure, and he accuses her of being unfaithful. Obviously shaken, Desdemona protests her innocence. After a terrible outburst of fury, Otello reverts to biting sarcasm as he dismisses her. Near collapsing, the hapless man invokes the mercy of God on his plight, then in somber determination resolves to pursue his course to the bitter end. When Iago brings on Cassio, Otello hides behind a column. During the jovial conversation between the two officers, Iago cleverly leads Cassio in and out of earshot of Otello. Thus Cassio's remarks about his girl-friend are interpreted by the Moor as being made about Desdemona. At last Cassio produces the handkerchief from his doublet. Pretending to admire it, Iago holds it so that Otello can clearly identify it, thus removing the last vestiges of doubt from the Moor's mind. While trumpet-flourishes announce the arrival of the Venetian delegate, Lodovico, Iago advises Otello to strangle his wife that very night. Amid the panoply of a festive reception Lodovico, in the name of the Republic of Venice, pays homage to Otello. Nearly insane with grief and fury, Otello reads the orders from his sovereign, directing him to Venice while Cassio is to assume command in Cyprus. Unable to control himself, Otello explodes in wild fury at Desdemona, throwing her to the ground in front of the horrified guests. He orders everyone out of the hall, then, reeling about and muttering incoherently, collapses completely. Unaware of the tragedy taking place inside the castle, the people of Cyprus hail their beloved governor. Contemplating the prostrate body of his master, Iago smugly gloats at the havoc he has wrought.

ACT IV. Desdemona, filled with evil foreboding, prepares to go to sleep. She orders Emilia to dress the bed with the same sheets that were used on her wedding-night, then hands her a ring as a keepsake. Sadly, she recalls a touching song she learned from a servant in her parents' home. After an emotion-charged farewell from her lady-in-waiting, Desdemona says her prayers and goes to bed. Entering silently, Otello approaches the bed and gazes at his sleeping wife. His tender kiss awakens her. Sternly, he tells her what he has come to accomplish. For the first time, he mentions Cassio's name, but her desperate denial of any wrong-doing goes unheeded. After strangling her, he is calm in the contemplation of what he has done. Emilia discovers the dreadful deed and calls for help. When Otello justifies his action by pointing to his wife's "adultery," Emilia, too late, tells the truth about the handkerchief. Thunderstruck, Otello realizes the enormity of his crime. Before anyone can prevent it, he stabs himself. Death overtakes him while he makes one last attempt to kiss the cold lips of his beloved wife.

CAST OF CHARACTERS

OTELLO, a Moor, General in the Venetian Army . . . . Tenor

IAGO, his Ensign . . . . Baritone

CASSIO, his Lieutenant . . . . Tenor

RODERIGO, a Venetian Gentleman . . . . Tenor

LODOVICO, Ambassador of the Venetian Republic . . . . Bass

MONTANO, predecessor of Otello in the Government of Cpyrus . . . . Bass

A HERALD . . . . Bass

DESDEMONA, Wife of Otello . . . . Soprano

EMILIA, Wife of Iago . . . . Mezzo-Soprano

Soldiers and Sailors of the Republic; Venetian Ladies and Gentlemen; Cypriot Men, Women and Children; Greek, Dalmatian and Albanian Soldiers; An Innkeeper; Four Inn Servers, People.

PLACE: A Seaport in Cyprus

TIME: The End of the 15th Century

SYNOPSIS OF SCENES

INDEX

ACT I.

OTELLO

ARRIGO BOITO

Giuseppe Verdi

English Version by
WALTER DUCLOUX

ACT I

Outside the castle. A tavern with an arbor. A view of the harbor. It is evening. A violent storm, lightning and thunder.

PIANO

Allegro agitato ♩ = 76.

(S'alza subito il sipario.)
(*The curtain rises quickly.*)

43686cx

Printed in U. S. A.

4

43686

6

scuo - - - - - te il ciel bi - e - co, co - - me un te - tro
fights _____ with sav-age fu - ry heav - - en's star-ry

Ah!
Ah!
Ah!
Ah!

Tut - to è
Through the
Tut - to è
Through the

vel..
light.

Ten.
fu - - mo! tut - - to è fuo - co! l'or - - ri-da ca -
foam and froth and fire wild, in-fer - - nal

Bassi
fu - - mo! tut - - to è fuo - co! l'or - - ri-da ca -
foam and froth and fire wild, in-fer - - nal

8ᵛᵃ bassa........

43686

po - - si ___ l'án - - co - -
As ___ Thou ___ al - - ways

po - - si ___ l'án - - co - -
As ___ Thou ___ al - - ways

po - - si ___ l'án - - co - -
As ___ Thou ___ al - - ways

ra fe - del.
didst be - fore!

ra fe - del.
didst be - fore!

ra fe - del.
didst be - fore!

Jago

È in - fran - to l'ar - ti - mon!
The mast has crashed on deck!

(Un lampo)
(flash of lightning)

Roderigo

Il ro-stro piom-ba su quel-lo scoglio!
The ship is lost and noth-ing can save it.

CHORUS

Sop.

A - i - -ta! a-
Al-might - -y, oh

Ten.

A - i - -ta! a-
Al-might - -y, oh

(Lampo)
(*Lightning*)

Jago

(a Roderigo)
(*to Roderigo*)

(L'al-vo fre - ne - -ti-co del mar sia la sua
(And so O - tel - -lo will go down and all is

i - ta!
help him!

i - ta!
help him!

(Lampo)
(*Lightning*)

48

43686

19

43686

CHORUS

sbar - co!
hur - ry!

Ev-
They've

Ten.

Ev - vi - - va!
They're land - - ing!

Bassi

vi - - va!
land - - ed.

Ev - vi - - - - -
Thank heav - - - - -

Sop.

Ev - vi - - - - -
Thank heav - - - - -

Ev - vi - - - - -
Thank heav - - - - -

Ev - vi - - - - -
Thank heav - - - - -

cresc. sempre

Vit - to - ria! Vit -
Vic - to - rious O -

strut-ti, se-pol-ti nel-l'or - ri - do ____ tu - mul-to piom-
based on the deep of the o - cean-floor! ____ Deep un-der the

strut-ti, se-pol-ti nel-l'or - ri - do ____ tu - mul-to piom-
based on the deep of the o - cean-floor! ____ Deep un-der the

to-ria!
tel-lo!

bàr.
sea.

A - vranno per *re-quie* la sfer-za dei
The crash-ing of thun-der, the howl-ing of

bàr.
sea.

A - vranno per *re-quie* la sfer-za dei
The crash-ing of thun-der, the howl-ing of

flut-ti, a-vran-no per *re - quie* la sfer-za dei flut-ti, la rid - da dei
tem-pests,the roar-ing of break-ers will sing them to sleep in the a - byss so

flut-ti, a-vran-no per *re - quie* la sfer-za dei flut-ti, la rid - da dei
tem-pests,the roar-ing of break-ers will sing them to sleep in the a - byss so

28

43686

J. bel - la, che nel se - gre - to de' tuoi so - gni a do - ri, pre - sto in
beau - ty, the se - cret cause of all your sleep - less tor - ment, will not

J. ug - gia ver - ran - no i fo - schi ba - ci di quel sel - vag - gio dal - le gon - fie
al - ways be rav - ished by em - brac - es and bru - tal kiss - es of that sav - age

dolce

J. lab - bra. Buon Ro - de - ri - go, a - mi - co tuo sin - ce - ro mi ti pro -
mon - ster. Good Ro - de - ri - go, you know how much my soul suf - fers at your

J. fes - so, nè in più for - te am - ba - scia soc - cor - rer - ti po - trei. Se un
sor - row. Let me find a way to bring com - fort to your heart. For

(indicando Cassio)
(pointing to Cassio)

guar _ da.
Watch him!

Quel l'az _ zi _ ma _ to ca _ pi _
That o _ ver _ bear _ ing lit _ tle

pp

ta _ no u _ sur _ pa il gra _ do mio, il gra _ do
cap _ tain took from___ me what is mine: my rank, a

poco cresc.

p

cresc.

(continua il passagio della bassa ciurma nel fondo)
(The movement of the crowd in the background continues)

mio che in cen _ to ben pu _ gna _ te bat _ ta _ glie ho me _ ri _
rank for which I risked my life in a hun _ dred bru _ tal en _

ta _ to;
coun _ ters.

tal fu il vo _ ler d'O _ tel _ lo,
Such is O _ tel _ lo's jus _ tice.

f

mf

Poco più lento

ed io ri - man - go di sua Mo - re - sca Si - gno - ria___ l'al - fie -
I stay the hum - ble foot - man of my Moor - ish mas - ter, oh glo -

Poco più lento

pp *ppp* *pp*

(dalla catasta incominciano ad alzarsi dei globi di fumo sempre più denso)
(Clouds of smoke, denser and denser begin to rise from the pile.)

re! Ma, com' è ver - che tu Ro - dri - go sei, così è pur
ry! But mark my word,- for what I say is this: Were I O-

f *pp* *f*

ve - ro che se il Mo - ro io fos - si, ve - der - mi non vor -
tel - lo I should hate to suf - fer so close___ to me a

p

rei d'at - tor - no un Ja - go. Se tu m'a - scol - ti...
man whose name is___ Ia - go! That's why I tell you . . .

ppp *f* *f*

del,   sul l'au - rea fiam - ma,   sul lie - to
love,   You that ca - ress me,   and kiss me

del,   sul l'au - rea fiam - ma,
love,   You that ca - ress me,

ciel,   sul - l'au - rea fiam - ma, sul lie - to
bove!   Flames that ca - ress me and kiss me

ciel,   sul - l'au - rea fiam - ma, sul lie - to
bove!   Flames that ca - ress me and kiss me

del,   sul - l'au - rea fiam - ma, sul lie - to
love,   Flames that ca - ress me and kiss me

co - ro   sof - fia l'ar - den - te   spi - ro del
light-ly,   Oh take me with you   to Heav'n a - -

sul lie - to co - ro   sof - fia l'ar - den - te spi - ro del
and kiss me light-ly,   take me a - long to Heav - en a -

co - ro sof - fia l'ar - den - te spi - ro del
light - ly, take me a - long to Heav - en a -

co - ro sof - fia l'ar - den - te spi - ro del
light - ly, take me a - long to Heav - en a -

co - ro sof - fia l'ar - den - te spi - ro del
light - ly, take me a - long to Heav - en a -

(Jago, Roderigo, Cassio e parecchi altri uomini d'arme intorno a un tavolo dove c'è del vino: parte in piedi, parte seduti)
(Iago, Roderigo, Cassio and some other soldiers are grouped round a table, on which there is wine; some sitting, some standing)

CC

Jago

Ro - de - ri - go, be - viam!   qua la taz - za, ca - pi -
Ro - de - ri - go, let's drink!   *Will you join us, Cap - tain*

Cassio

(ritirando il bicchiere)
(moving back his glass)

Non be - vo più.   (avvicinando il boccale alla tazza di Cassio)   No.
I drink no more.   *(drawing the can to the glass of Cassio)*   *No.*

ta - - no.   In - go - ia que - sto sor - so.
Cas - - sio?   *To-night you can't re - fuse it.*

Jago

Guarda! oggi impazza tut - ta Cipro!   è u - na notte di gio - ia, dunque...
Cap-tain, 'tis a night we shall re - mem-ber,   and all Cy-prus is feast-ing. There-fore . . .

Cassio

Ces - sa.   Già m'ar - de il cer - vel - lo per un nap - po vuo - ta - to.
Leave me!   My head is a-whirl al-though I drank but one cup - ful!

Sì, an -
Yet to -

43686

56

43686

43686

72

pp e molto staccato

43686

88

Scene II

sen-no, sguainan-do l'ar-me s'avven-ta-no fu-ren-ti.
Sa-tan, they drew their weap-ons and locked in bru-tal com-bat.

A-ves-si io pri-ma stron-ca-ti i piè che qui m'ad-
I should have rath-er both my feet cut off than be a

Otello

Cas-sio, come ob-lia-sti te stes-so a tal se-gno?
Cas-sio, how could you so dis-grace your po-si-tion?

dus-ser!
wit-ness.

Più mosso ♩ = 120.

Mon-ta-no...
Mon-ta-no...

Cassio

Gra-zia... per-don... par-lar non so...
Par-don... for-give... I can-not speak... *(sostenuto da un soldato)*
Montano *(leaning on a soldier)*

Son fe
I am

Più mosso ♩ = 120.

RR (la scena si vuota. Otello fa cenno agli uomini colle fiaccole che lo accompagnavano di rientrare nel Castello)
(The stage is nearly empty. Othello beckons to the torchbearers to reenter the castle)

Scene III (restano soli Otello e Desdemona)
(Othello and Desdemona alone remain)

Lo stesso movimento ♩ = 66.
con espressione

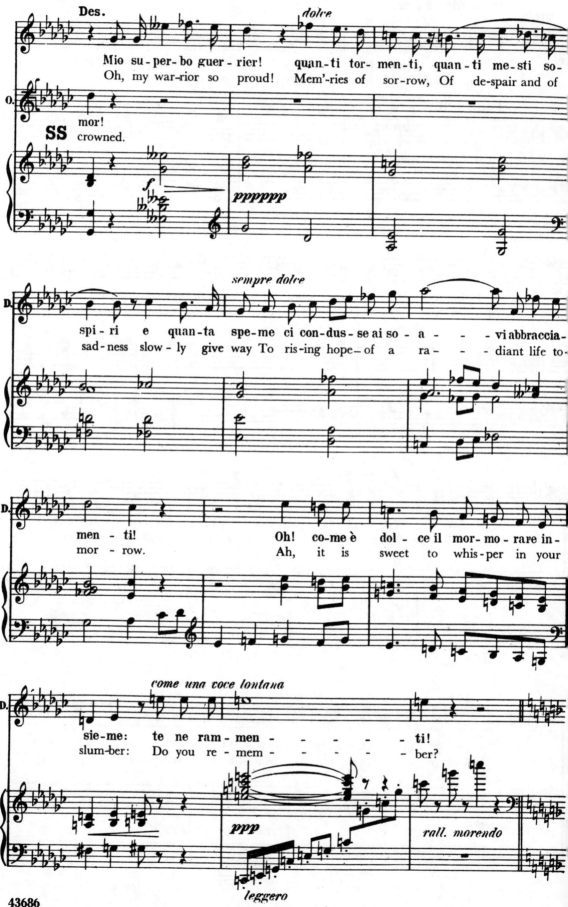

SS

Des. *dolce*

Mio su-per-bo guer-rier! quan-ti tor-men-ti, quan-ti me-sti so-
Oh, my war-rior so proud! Mem'-ries of sor-row, Of de-spair and of

O.

SS mor!
crowned.

f *pppppp*

sempre dolce

spi-ri e quan-ta spe-me ci con-dus-se ai so-a - - -vi abbraccia-
sad-ness slow-ly give way To ris-ing hope-of a ra - - -diant life to-

men - ti! Oh! co-me è dol - ce il mor-mo-rare in-
mor - row. Ah, it is sweet to whis-per in your

come una voce lontana

sie-me: te ne ram-men - - - - -ti!
slum-ber: Do you re-mem - - - - - ber?

ppp *rall. morendo*

leggero

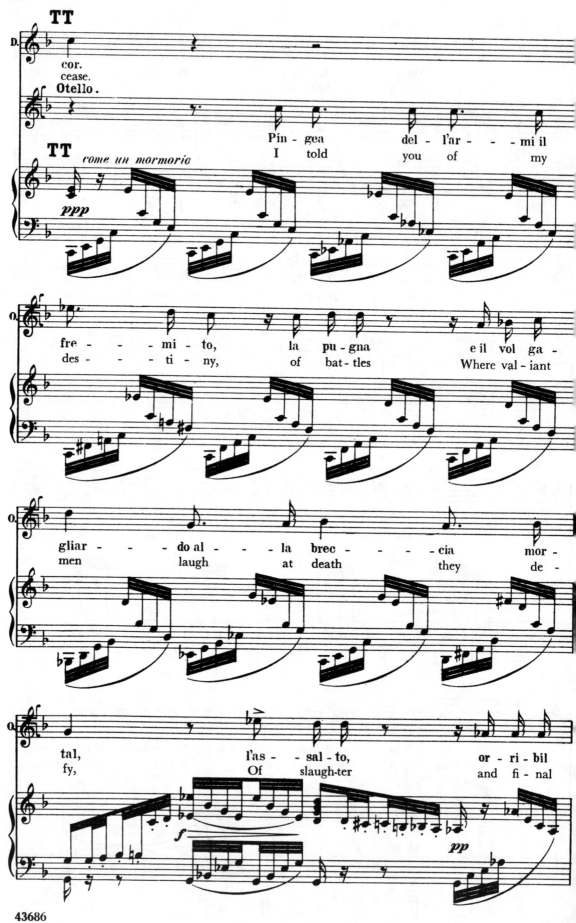

e - de - ra,　col l'u - - gna al ba - - lu -
vic - to - ry,　of sol - - diers march - - ing

p　*poco cresc.*

ar - - - do　e il si - bi - lan - - te
on - - - ward　A - gain to win　or

sempre cresc. - - - - - - - - - - ff

Des.　*legato*

Poi mi gui - da - vi ai
Then you would guide me

stral!
die.　**Tempo I.**

ff *pp*　*pp dolce con espressione*

ful - gi - di de - ser - ti,　al - l'ar - se a - re - ne, al
far a - cross the o - cean,　There, where the sun will for-

legato

spir; scendean sul-le mie te-ne-bre la gloria, il pa-ra-
eyes. Like dia-monds they would shine on me, like bril-liant rays from

di - so_____ e gli a - stri a be - ne -
heav - en,_____ out of the star - lit

Ed io ve - dea fra le tue tem - - pie o -
And I would no - tice in your face so

scu - re splen - der del ge - nio l'e - te - rea bel -
ten - der Burn - ing a fire so in - tense and so

(il cielo si sarà tutto rasserenato: si vedranno alcune stelle e sul lembo dell'orizzonte il riflesso ceruleo della nascente luna)
(*The sky is now quite clear; some stars are shining and on the horizon the reflex of the rising moon is seen*)

te - mo, te - mo che più non mi sa - rà con - ces - so que-
heart that fate can no long - er hold an earth-ly prom - ise. In

st'at - ti - mo di - vi - no nel - l'i - gnoto avve - - nir del mio de - sti -
dark-ness lies en - shroud-ed what the Lord will be - - stow up-on O - tel -

XX Des.

Di - sper - da il ciel gli af - fan - ni e A - mor non
I vowed be - fore the al - tar: Our love shall

XX no.
lo.

pp

mu - ti col mu - tar de - gl'an - - ni.
ev - er grow and nev - er fal - - ter.

A que - sta tua pre -
The an - gels sing be -

pp

(s'avviano abbracciati verso il castello)
(exeunt, clinging close to each other, towards the castle.)

lo!
lo!

de!
us!

dim. allarg. un poco

In tempo

una corda sola

ppp legatissimo

dim. sempre

morendo

End of the 1st Act.

ACT II

A Hall on the Ground Floor of the Castle

Two colonnades, one on each side, through which we look out into the garden.

Scene I

(S'alza il sipario)
(The curtain rises)

Jago (al di qua del verone, a Cassio)
(in the hall, to Cassio)

Non ti crucciar.
Be of good cheer!

senza misura

Se cre-di a me, tra po-co, fa - rai ri - torno ai fol-leg-gianti a-mo-ri di Mon-na Bian-
I am quite sure in less than a week you will kiss her a-gain, your sweet lit-tle love,— Bian-

senza misura, col canto

a tempo

ca,— al - tie-ro ca - pi - ta - no, coll' el - sa d'o-ro e col bal-feo fre -
ca;— and, e - ven more im - por-tant, you will be Cap-tain once a - gain, be -

a tempo

Allegro sostenuto ♩ = 96.

lunga

(allontanandosi dal verone senza più guardar Cassio che sarà scomparso fra gli alberi)
(he comes forward without taking further notice of Cassio who disappears amongst the trees.)

J.

di - o:
E - vil.

Allegro sost. ♩ = 96.

attacca subito

Cre -
Yes, —

J.

- do in un Dio cru - del che m'ha cre - a - to si - mi - le a
__ I be - lieve that I was made the like - ness of one on

sè,
high,

J.

e che nel - l'i - ra io no - - - - - - - mo.
some-one him-self a mon - - - - - - - ster.

ff

aspramente

f

Jago

Dal - la vil - ta d'un ger - me o d'un a -
Foul is the seed I come from, filth - y and

pppp

tò - mo vi - le son na - to.
rot -ten is all that's in me.

pesanti

Son scel - le - ra - to per - chè son uo - mo, e sen - to il
He is e - ter - nal and is in - fer - nal, and I must

fango o - ri - gi - na - rio in me. Sì! que-st'è la mia
go my e - vil path with him. Yes, this is Ia - go's

ml.

E

fè!
creed:

E

dim.

l'uom — gio - co d'i - ni - qua sor - - te dal
faith: We are but fools of for - - tune, of

ger - - - me del - la cul - - la
blind_____ and sense - less for - - tune,

al ver - me del - l'a -
our life's a stu - pid

vel.
farce.

Poco più lento

Vien_ do - po
Death_ in the

tan - ta ir - ri - sion la Mor - te.
end will pull the fi - nal cur - tain.

E poi?
And then?

e poi?
What then?

La Morte è il Nul - la
And then there's noth - ing!

Allegro più di prima ♩ = 104.

è vec - chia fo la il
'Tis all a mon - strous

3686

(Si vede passare nel giardino Desdemona con Emilia. Iago si slancia al verone, al di là del quale è appostato Cassio
(Desdemona and Emilia are seen to enter the garden. Iago goes toward the terrace beyond which
Cassio has taken his position.)

J.

Già con - ver - sa - no in - sie - me...
What a friend-ly en - coun-ter!

ed es - sa in - cli - na, sor - ri - den - do, il bel
Her love-ly face is close to his and she is

(si vedono ripassare nel giardino Cassio e Desdemona)
(Cassio and Desdemona are seen passing backwards and forwards in the garden.)

vi - so.   Mi basta un lam - po   sol di quel sor - ri -
smil-ing.   One sin-gle ray of   such a charm-ing smile will

so   per   tra - sci - na - re O - tel-lo al-la ru - i -
do   to   warp the great O - tel-lo's heart for-ev -

Scene III

cen-no por-ta - va al-la mia spo-sa.   Sì, das-sen-no.   Nel credi o -
tween in the ear-ly days of our court-ship.   Yes, I'm cer-tain.   Is he dis -

Dassenno?
You're cer-tain?

ne - sto?   Che a-scon - di nel tuo co - re?
hon- est?   Why did you ask this ques-tion?

(imitando Otello)
(imitating Othello)

O - ne - sto?
Dis - hon -est?

„Che a-scon-do in cor, si - gno - re?"   Pel
'For -give me my sug - ges - tion!'   May

Che a-scon-do in cor, si - gno - re?
For -give me my sug - ges - tion!

co - ra! Ma di che t'ac - co - ra - vi? / no - mi - ni Cas-sio e al-
won-der.' Tell me then, what made you won-der? / **You spoke of Cas-sio and**

lo - ra tu cor - ru - ghi la fron-te.
then I saw your brow get fur-rowed.

sempre cresc.

Jago. Suv - via,_____ par - la se m'a - mi.
Speak out_____ if you be loy - al!

Voi sa - pe - te ch'io
Do not doubt_ that I'm

N Moderato ♩ = 88.   *marcato*

Dun-que sen-za ve - la - mi t'e - spri - mi e senza am-
This is why I com - mand you: Tell me all of your

v'a - mo.
loy - al!

N Moderato ♩ = 88.

3686

va no so-spet-tar nul-la gio-va. Pria del
shall not be a prey to sus-pi-cion. Ere I

dub-bio l'in-da-gi-ne, do-po il dub-bio la
doubt I shall ver-i-fy. Af-ter doubt I want

pro-va, do-po la pro-va (O-
proof.___ And when I have it (for

tel-lo ha sue leg-gi su-pre-me), a-mo-re e ge-lo-
this is the es-sence of jus-tice) a-way at once with

sia va-dan dis-per - - si in - sie-me.
jeal-ou-sy and love___ to - geth-er!

(con piglio più ardito)
(more *frank in manner*)

Jago

Un tal pro-po-sto spez - - za di mie lab - bra il sug -
A no - ble word, my lord,___ which breaks the seal up-on my

Lo stesso movimento Allegro moderato ♩ = 66.

(molto lontano)
(*in the garden*) pp *dolce*

Sopr. I.

Do - ve guar - di splen - do-no rag - - gi, av-vam-pan
Pure and ra - diant out of the sky, Like sun-shine

Sopr. II. III. pp

Do - ve guar - di splen - - do-no rag - gi, av-vam - pan
Pure and ra - diant out of the sky,___ Like sun - shine

Ten. pp

Do - ve guar - - - di___
Pure and ra - - - diant___

Bass. pp

Do - - ve guar - - - di___
Pure and ra - - - diant___

J.

gel-lo. Non parlo ancor di pro-va; pur, ge-ne-ro - so O-
lips. I do not speak of proof yet . . . But, no-ble lord and

P Lo stesso movimento Allegro moderato ♩ = 66.

pp

(Cornamuse) (*Bag-pipes*)

43686

ta - re, pa - dri, bim - bi, spo - se ven-gono a can-
spring, Your smile has called us here To praise you and to

ta - re, pa - dri, bim - bi, spo - se ven-gono a can-
spring, Your smile has called us here To praise you and to

no ____ nu - vo - - le di fio -
en - ly eye, Oh, so be - guil -

no ____ nu - vo - - le di fio -
en - ly eye, Oh, so be - guil -

sde-mo - na, un det-to può ri-con-dur la fe - de, può afferma - re il so -
guard-ed word, one ges-ture per-haps will prove her guilt-less... or con-firm your sus -

tar.
sing.

tar.
sing.

(Si vede ricomparire Desdemona nel giardino, dalla vasta apertura del fondo: essa è circon-
data da donne dell'isola, da fanciulli, da marinai cipriotti e albanesi, che si avanzano e le
offrono fiori e rami fioriti ed altri doni. Alcuni s'accompagnano, cantando, sulla *guzla*
(una specie di mandòla), altri hanno delle piccole arpe ad armacollo.)
(*Desdemona is seen to return to the garden through the large opening at the back;
she is surrounded by women, children, and Cypriot and Albanian sailors, who come
forward in turn offering her flowers and other gifts. They sing, accompanying
themselves, some on the guzla a kind of mandoline and others on small harps.*)

ri.
ing.

ri.
ing.

(come prima sottovoce)
(*softly as before*)

spet - to. Ec - co - la... vi - gi - la - - te.
pi - cion. Here she is. Watch her close - - ly!

p con eleganza

Do - ve guar-di splen-do-no rag - - gi,av-vam-pan
Pure and ra-diant out of the sky, Like sun - shine

Do-ve guar-di splen - do-no rag - gi,av-vam- pan
Pure and ra-diant out of the sky,— Like sun - shine

8 Tenors.

Do - ve guar - - di _____
Pure and ra - - diant _____

6 Basses.

Do - -ve guar - - di _____
Pure and ra - - diant _____

pp dolciss.

138

43686

cór.
prayer!

Quel can - to mi con - qui - de.
Their ten - der song re - lieves me.

mor.
more!

mor.
more!

mor.
more!

mor.
more!

mor.
more!

- di, i vostri in-fran-ge - rò so-avi ac-cor-di.)
- ed. Yes, through me their sweet tune will be end-ed!)

(Finito il Coro, Desdemona bacia la testa d'alcuni tra i fanciulli, e alcune donne le baciano il lembo della veste, ed essa porge una borsa ai marinai. Il Coro s'allontana. Desdemona, seguita poi da Emilia, entra nella sala e s'avanza verso Otello.)
(When the singing is over Desdemona kisses some of the children, some of the women kiss the hem of her gown. She gives a purse to the sailors. Exit Chorus slowly. Desdemona followed by Emilia comes forward into the hall where Othello stands.)

dolce

morendo

legato
pp

pp

poco rall.

Scene IV

Lo stesso movimento

158

43686

so - - -no u - mi - le e man - su -
guilt - - - less, ea - - ger to serve my

Emilia

(sottovoce a Jago)
(aside to Iago)

(Qual fro - de scor - gi? Ti leg - go in
What are you plan - ning? I do not

col - to.
hold - ing!

e - - ta;
mas - - ter!

vol - to.
trust you.

for - se per - chè di - scen - do nel - la val - le_ de -
May - be the pass - - ing years have made me bit - ter_ and_

T'op - po - ni a vô - to quand' io co -
Why this re - luc - tance when I com-

170

43686

sa- -gio?
pi- -cion?
E- ro bal -do, giu-
Bright and hap- py,   de-

li- vo... Nul- la sa- pe- vo an- cor; io non sen-
lir- ious... Bliss- ful and free of doubt I could en-

cresc.

p dolciss. *f*

ti- vo sul suo cor- po di - vin che m'in- na- mo- ra e sui
joy her splen- did beau- ty and charm, drunk with de- sire.___ In the

pp

lab- bri men- da- ci gli ar- den- ti ba- ci di
glow of her kiss- es how could I taste the lips of

portando la voce

Cas- sio! Ed o- - ra! ed o- - ra...
Cas- sio? 'Tis o- - ver... for- ev- - er!

cresc.

43686

fat - - to sem - - - - - - pre vi sfug - gi-
lov - - ers kind - - - - ly re - veal them-

rà?
selves?

Ma pur se gui - da è la ra - gione al
And yet I tell you: I think I can con-

ve - ro, u - na sì for - te con - get - tu - ra ri - ser - bo che per
vince you, giv - ing you proof of such un - ques - tioned as - sur - ance that your

po - co al la cer - tez - za vi con - du - ce. U - di - te.
doubts_will yield at once and you will know the truth. For in - stance:

Andantino ♪=112.

(avvicinandosi molto ad Otello e sotto voce.)
(he goes closely up to Othello; in a whisper.)
mezza voce

É - ra la not - te, Cas-sio dor - mi - a, gli sta - vo ac
Long af - ter mid - night, Cas-sio was sleep - ing While I lay

can - to. Con in - ter - rot - te vo - ci tra - di - a l'in - ti - mo ir
near him, When in his slum - ber soft - ly he whis - pered, Yet I coul

can - to. Le lab - bra len - te, len - te, mo - ve - a, nel l'ab - ban
hear him; His lips were part - ed, smil - ing in rap - ture; Sigh - ing in

do - no del so - gno ar - den - te; e al - lor di - ce - a, con fle - bil
ec - sta - sy he lay dream-ing. Clear-ly I heard it, what he was

col - pa! / heav-en!

Un sogno che ri - ve - la un fat - to. / A dream which is a rev - e - la - tion!

Io non nar-rai che un sogno. / 'Twas but a dream, re - mem-ber!

Un / A

Più mosso ♪ = 144.

so - - gno che può dar for - ma di pro - va ad al - tro in - / dream, air - y and vague, may lead us on___ to firm - er

Più mosso ♪ = 144.

Otello · **Più lento**

E qual? / How so?

di - zio. / mat-ter.

senza misura

Ta - lor ve - de - ste in ma - no di De - / Do you re - mem-ber in Des-de - mo - na's

Più lento

pp senza misura

Per la Mor - te e per l'o - scu - ro mar ster-mi-na -
you, im - mor - tal sea a - round me, deep, si - lent and

- tor! Di - ra e d'im - - pe - to tre -
dark: Hear my vow on my sa - cred

men - do pre - - sto fia che
hon - or: Ven - - geance be my

(levando le mani al ciel
(he lifts up his hand)

sfol - go - ri que - sta man ch'io le - vo e
last re - solve, and this hand, it shall a -

ppp

cresc.

mf

196

sten - do.
ven - geance!

Dio   ven - di - ca -
So   help me,   o

sten - do.
ven - geance!

Dio   ven - di - ca -
So   help me,   o

tor!
God!

tor!
God!

pesante

Fine dell' Atto secondo.
End of the second Act.

Act III

The great Hall of the Castle

The main hall in the castle; to the right a wide portico, leading to a smaller hall; to the rear an alcove.

(s'alza il sipario.)
(Curtain rises.)

Scene I

sco‿sto scru‿ta‿te i mo‿di suoi, le sue pa‿ro‿le, i laz‿zi, i
hid‿ing whence you can see us both. Ob‐serve him close‐ly, his fea‐tures and

lunga

gesti. Pa‐zi‿en‿te sia‐te o la pro‐va vi sfugge.
ges‐tures! But be pa‐tient, mas‐ter, or the proof will es‐cape you!

♩ = 72

(dicendo *io vado*, s'allontana come per escire, poi
s'arresta e si riavvicina ad Otello per dirgli l'ultima
parola.)

(*As he says "I leave you", he moves away as if to
leave, but stops and returns to Othello, to say
the last word.*)

lento

Ec‐co Des‐de‐mo‐na. Finger convie‐ne... io va‐do. Il faz‐zo‐let‐to...
Here comes Des‐de‐mo‐na! Be on your guard now! I leave you! Re‐mem‐ber the ker‐chief!

col canto

Otello

(Jago esce)
(*exit Jago*)

Va! vo‐lon‐tie‐ri o‐bli‐a‐to l'a‐vrei.
Go! Oh, that ker‐chief I should glad‐ly for‐get!

ppp subito

Scene II

di - a   lo stame ar - ca - - - - no:
tex - - ture   an in - can - ta - - - - tion,

i - vi è   ri - po - sta   l'al - ta ma -
doom - - ing   the one   who'd   lose   or a -

lì - - a   d'un ta - li - sma - - - no.
buse   it   to   dark dam - na - - - tion.

Ba - da!   smar - rir - lo,   oppur do - nar - lo   è ria sven -
There - fore: be   care - ful!   If you have lost it,   you will re -

E-ster - re - fat - ta fis - so
My brow turns pale with ter-ror.

lo sguardo tuo tre - mendo,
You seem to speak of trea-son.

in te parla u - na
I hear the sounds of

Fu - ria, la sento e non l'in - tendo. Mi guar-da!
mad - ness, So fright-en-ing, yet with-out rea-son. Be - hold me!

Poco più animato ♩=84

con passione

il vol - to e l'a - ni - ma ti svelo; il co - re in - fran - to ni scru -
My eyes, not words, shall now im-plore you! My heart lies o - pen be - fore

Come prima ♩=72

pp cantabile

ta... io pre - go il cie - lo per te con que-sto
you. I cry to heav - en in an-guished des - o -

pian - to, per te con que-ste stil - le co - cen - ti a - spergo il
la - tion, My eyes be - dewed and blind, Let your tears tell my lord for

animando

suol. Guarda le pri - me la - gri - me, guarda le pri - me
me, Eyes that have nev - er lied be - fore, Tears that I've nev - er

petro. spo - so mi - o!
mand of you, O - tel - -lo!

Ah! De - sdemona! In - die - tro! in -
Ah! Des - de - mo - na, go from me! Go

mf

molto staccato

die - tro! in - die - tro!
from me! Go from me!

f

pp

Des.

Tu pur pian - gi? e ge - men - do freni del cor lo
You are weep-ing, and your heart is tor-tured in si - -lent

dim.

Opp.

gia— — — — — na che è la pet....Like the
strum— — — — — pet....Like the

(cupo)

(cupo e terribile)
(in a hollow and terrible voice)   voce soffocata

gia— — — — — na che è la spo-sa d'O- tel- - -lo.
strum— — — — — pet...Like the wife of O- tel- - -lo!

pppp

(Otello sforza con un'inflessione del braccio, ma senza scomporsi, Desdemona ad escire. Poi ritorna verso il centro della scena nel massimo grado dell'abbattimento)
(Othello with a motion of his arm, but without changing his position pushes Desdemona out of the room. Then he returns to the centre of the stage in deep dejection)

M **Come prima** ♩= 132

ff

dim.

dim.

pp

Scene III

Adagio ♩ = 66

estremamente p

Otello
(voce soffocata) *pppp*

Dio! mi po - te - vi scagliar tutti i ma - li del - la mi -
God, Thou couldst try me with all the be-reave-ments If Thy dis -

se - ria, del - la ver - go - gna,
plea-sure I have brought on me.

228

43686

230

43686

(Jago, appena condotto Otello al verone, corre verso il fondo del peristiglio)
(Having led Othello to the terrace Jago runs to the portico.)

Scene V

Jago
(incontra Cassio che esita ad entrare)
(he meets Cassio who enters)

(a Cassio)
(to Cassio)

R Sostenuto ♩ = 60

Vie - ni; l'au - la è de -
Come now! No one can

ser - ta. Ti - nol - tra, o - Ca - pi -
hear us. How are you, my wor - thy

Cassio

Questo no - me d'o - nor suo - na ancor va - no per me.
You have men-tioned the cause why I am sad and dis-tressed.

ta - - no. Fu
cap - - tain? Your

236

tà _____ vin - - ce chi ri - de. Ah! ah! (ridèndo)
clare! _____ Win - -ning means grin -ning! Ha, ha! (laughing)

Ah!
Ha,

Otello (dal vernone)
(in the colonnade)

(L'em-pio tri - on - - fa, il suo scher - no m'uc - ci -
(This hell-ish laugh - - ter like a dag - ger im - pales

ah!
ha!

- de; Dio _____ fre - na l'an - - sia_che in
me, fu - - ry as - sails___ me_ and

(con disperazione)
(in despair)

co - - - - re mi - sta!___)
dark - - - - est de - spair!___)

(mettendo le mani dietro la schiena perche Otello possa osservare il fazzoletto)
(holding the handkerchief behind him so as to let Othello see it.)

stel - lo   per - do - no gli an - ge - li l'au - reo - la e il
lute you!   An - gels them - selves could not with - stand your

Otello (avvicinandosi assai al fazzoletto, dietro le spalle di Jago e nascosto dalla prima colonna)
(looking at the handkerchief and standing just behind Iago hidden by the first column)

(È quel - lo!   è quel - lo!
(The ker - chief!   I see it!

vel.
charm.

(a parte sotto voce)
(aside very softly)

Ru - i - na e Mor - te!   Tutto è
The world has end - ed!   All is

(to himself)

(O - ri-glia O - tel - lo.)
(Look here, O - tel - lo!)

spen - to!   a - more e duol.   L'al - ma mia nis - sun più
o - ver,   both love and pain,   and my heart has turned to

morendo

cupo

J. ra _ gna do _ ve il tuo cor ca _ sca, si la _ gna, s'im-pi _ glia e
spin-ning, pre - tend - ing to play, Spi- ders are win-ning to kill their

Otello (nascosto dietro la colonna e guardando di tratto in tratto il fazzoletto nelle mani di Cassio.)
(hidden behind the column and looking at the handkerchief in Cassio's hand.)

Otello: Tra _ di _ men _ _ _ to, tra _ di _ men _ _ _ to, tra-di-
Her be - tray _ _ _ al, her be - tray _ _ _ al, her be -

Cassio Più bian _ co, più lie _ ve che
You're soft - er and light-er, You

J. muor. Trop _ _ po l'am _ _ mi _ _ ri,
prey, Let - ting it quiv _ - er,

O. men _ _ to, la tua pro _ va, la_____ tua
tray _ _ al, it is prov _ en, prov _ - en,

C. fioc _ co di ne _ ve, che nu _ be tes _
shim - mer much bright - er Than clouds white and

J. trop _ _ po la guar _ di, ba _ da ai de _
flit - ter and fly Un - - til it will

ff e legato

pro - - va spa ven - to - - - -
prov - - en clear as day,

su - ta dal l'au re del ciel.
shin y That float through the skies.

li - ri va ni e bu giar di.
shiv er, flick er and die.

- - - - - - - sa mo stri al
yes, clear as

Mi - - ra - col,
O lin - en,

Ah, ba - da,
I'll tell you:

Sol
day.

mi - - ra - co lo va - - -
I know not who brought

questa è una ra gna do-ve il tuo cuor ca - sca, si
Pret - ti - ly spin-ning, pre-tend-ing to play, Spi - ders are

251

43686

252

43686

J. spet - ti De - sde - mo - na si mo - stri a quei Mes - se - ri.
pi - cion, Des - de - mo - na should be with you to greet them.

(Jago esce dalla porta di sinistra: Otello s'avvia verso
il fondo per ricevere gli Ambasciatori)
(exit Iago right. Othello goes towards back to re-
ceive the Ambassadors.)

Otello

Sì, qui l'ad - du - ci.
Yes, go and call her!

(Trombe interne)
(Trumpets behind)

cresc.

cresc.

f

ff

Scene VII (Entrano Jago, Lodovico, Roderigo, l'Araldo.— Desdemona con Emilia — Dignitari della Republica Veneta — Gentiluomini e Dame — Soldati — Trombettieri, poi Cassio.)
(Enter Iago, Lodovico, Roderigo, the Herald.— Desdemona with Emilia — Dignitaries of the Venetian Republic — Gentlemen and Ladies, Soldiers, Trumpeters, afterwards Cassio.)

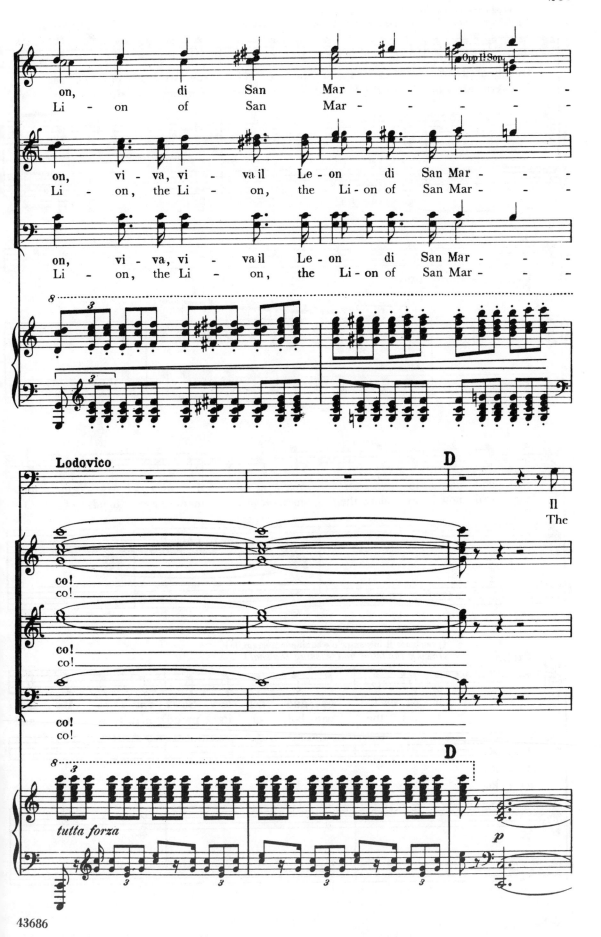

43686

Scene VIII

270

43686

cor. / blind.
Quel Sol_____ se - re - no e / The sun,_____ so high a -

vi - vi - do_____ che al - lie - - ta il cie-lo e il / bove the world_____ In all_____ its ra - diant

ma - re / splen - - dor,
non può_____ sciugar le a - / No sol - - ace can it

ma - re stil - - le del mio do lor, le amare stille del mio do- / ten - der To my bro - ken___heart, No sol-ace for my grief I shall ev-er

col canto

274

43686

ge - sto, trat - tiene in pet-to il ge - mi-to___
sigh - ing. Nev - er her lips so white - ly drawn___

di - ta; già___ di mia sor-te il cul - mi - ne
splen - - dor. Star - tled, I see how star - less___ night

stin, il de - stin; l'angiol so - a - ve e bion - - do scom -
heart, ah, my heart, For with my love to - mor - - row will

d'i - ra, es - sa la faccia e - te - - rea
vile___ her? Weep - ing in des - per - a - - tion

Pietà!___
Oh Lord!___

Pietà!___
Oh Lord!___

dolcissimo

dì   sul mio   sor - ri - - - so   fio -
dream   of love has   end - - - ed,   Of

la - gri - ma si   fran - - ge
tears   a bit - ter   riv - - er

L'eb - bra for - tu - - na in - cal - - - za
Fate writes a won - - drous sto - - - ry:

L'an - - giol so - - a - ve   scom -
My   heart in_____ de - spair will

ne - rea scuo - te a - ne - lan - do d'i - - ra,   es - sa la fac - cia e -
a - tion so cruel - ly he re - vile her? Weep - ing in des - per -

tà!
awe.   Pie - tà, pie -
                                   I   stand in

tà!
awe.   Pie - tà, pie -
                                   I   stand in

Mi - ste - - - - ro!
What hap - - - - pened?

Mi - ste - - - - ro!
What hap - - - - pened?

pp staccato assai

43686

314

Scene IX

(Restano soli Otello e Jago)
(Othello and Iago alone remain)

(ritto e con gesto d'orrendo trionfo, indicando il corpo inerte d'Otello)
(*standing erect and pointing with horrible triumph to the motionless body of Othello*)

Vi - va! vi - va! vi - va O - tel -
Glor-y, glor - y! Hail, O - tel -

Vi - va! vi - va! vi - va O - tel -
Glor-y, glor - y! Hail, O - tel -

lo!
lo!

lo!
lo!

ff

8 basso

Fine dell' Atto terzo.
End of Act III.

ACT IV

The Bedroom of Desdemona

A bed, a prayer bench, a table, several chairs and mirrors. A burning lamp is
suspended in front of a statue of the Virgin above the prayer bench. A door to the right.
It is night. A lamp is burning on the table.

car - mi e d'at-ten-der-lo.
rest and to wait for him.

E-mi - lia, te ne
E-mi - lia, let me

a tempo

pre - go, di-sten-di sul mio let-to la mia can - di - da
ask you: Be-fore you go to sleep, re - place these sheets with those that

pp a tempo

ve - ste nu - zi - a - - - le.
lay there at my wed - - - ding!

(Emilia eseguisce)
a tempo (Emilia busies herself about the bed)

p

con passione

Sen - ti.
Lis - ten:

Se pria di te mo - rir do -
If God would have me die be -

43686

sot - to la mal-va-gia sor - te;   per noi, per noi tu

Lost in deep-est woe and dark-ness!   Ah, pray for us in

pre - - ga, pre-ga sem-pre e nel l'o - ra del-la

heav - - en, now and for-ev-er! Grant us Thy mer-cy that we may

mor - te no - - stra, pre-ga per noi, pre-ga per noi, pre-

die for-giv - - en, Moth-er of God, Moth-er of God, oh

(Resta ancora inginocchiata e appoggiando la fronte sull'inginocchiatoio ripete
mentalmente l'orazione di cui non s'odono che le prime e le ultime parole.)
(She remains kneeling, resting her head on the prie-Dieu and repeating her prayer only the first and last words of which are audible.)

ga.   A - ve Ma-ria..

pray!   Hail to Thee, Ma-ry . . .

Scene III

Poco più mosso ♩ = 80

Otello (Alla prima nota comparirà Otello sulla soglia di una porta segreta.)
(At the first note Othello is seen standing on the threshold of a secret door.)

Poco più mosso ♩ = 80

342

Se vi sov-vie - - ne di qual-che col-pa com-
If you re-mem - - ber a crime for which you had for-

mes - sa che atten-da gra-zia dal ciel, im-plo-ra-te la to-
got - ten to ask the mer-cy of God: Do it now with-out wait-

BB **Lo stesso Movimento**
Desdemona

Per - chè?
My lord!

sto. T'af-fret-ta! Uc - ci-de-re non
ing! Well, do it! I should not kill your

BB **Lo stesso Movimento**

Fine dell' Opera.
End of the Opera.